The Kama Sutra Sex Positions: The Book Of Hot Sex Positions

Wendy Espino Menchaca

Copyright

The Kama Sutra

Dedication

Dedicated to all sex lovers
who wish to enjoy more sex.

The Kama Sutra

Table of Contents

Introduction

The most revered and important work on love and sex is
generally regarded as the Kamasutra.

Sanskrit, the literary language of ancient India at the
time, was used by a Hindu scholar by the name of
Vtsyyana to record it in the fourth century following the
birth of Christ..

However, what adventures lie ahead for you?

If you want more than just a few seconds of enjoyment
from your spouse, some of these abilities might be able
to assist you in maintaining a healthy connection with

them. The key is to combine a fulfilling sexual life with a healthy sense of adventure.

Therefore, get ready to perfect some of these abilities and become an attractive partner.

What precisely is the Kamasutra?

It is often referred to for its sexual positions, the Kama Sutra is an ancient Indian text that covers a variety of topics related to courting, marriage, and love-making.

Is the Kamasutra a literature on sexuality?

The majority of people are under the impression that the Kama Sutra is primarily concerned with sexual matters; yet, its primary focus is on the philosophy and theory of love. It touches on issues such as the search for a life mate, flirtation, and the fundamentals of romantic love. However, it is most famous for its explanations of the many sex positions that might be assumed. Additionally,

if you're searching for some sexual inspo, this is a
fantastic place to begin your search.
Which sex positions recommended in the Kamasutra
are the most straightforward?

The Kamasutra Positions

1. Straightforward man on top front entry position with the female.

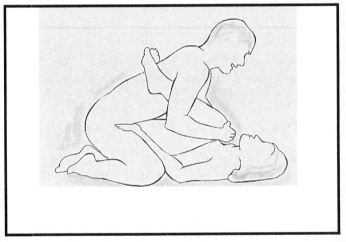

The man kneels in front of the woman as she
is positioned on her back with her legs drawn
toward her chest, and the lady lies on her
stomach. After that, she will be able to prop

her feet up on his chest while he supports her knees with his forearms. After that, the lady might hold the man's thighs and pull him closer to her for a more intense sexual experience. The deeper he presses down on her knees, the more pleasure he gives her in that position.

A sexual position that does not demand a great deal of flexibility and is reasonably easy to perform.

2. The Traverse

Only males who are extraordinarily strong and flexible should attempt this exercise; the woman will cross over his body while he acts as a bridge. After that, she is able to ascend and descend by pushing off the ground with her feet, which is not for the faint of heart.

To keep everything moving smoothly, we recommend always having some lubrication on hand.

3. The Clutch

The grip demands the woman to assume a position that is quite similar to that of the missionary, in which she lays on her back and raises her hips ever-so-slightly (it may be more comfortable for the woman to place a cushion under her bottom). The male then positions himself between her legs, and she moves her pelvis in a side-to-side motion while he does so.

Simple and effective when you're not in the mood to expend a lot of energy

4. The Day Pleaser

The guy is positioned so that he is lying on his side, while the lady is positioned so that she is lying on her back at a right angle to her partner. She places her knees over his hip in a position that makes it easier for her to penetrate him.

Extremely simple, making it an ideal activity for a sedentary Sunday afternoon or for times when you want to take things a little bit easier on your partner during a lengthy sex session.

Why not purchase a handheld massager for the two of you so that you can unwind even further?

5. The Cowgirl

A move that is quite similar to the reverse cowgirl is called the rider. In this move, the lady rides on top of the male while turning her back to him. After that, she slides up and down on his knees while leaning forward and supporting herself on his knees. By maintaining his grip on the woman's waist, the man can likewise maintain control over the penetration.

It does not demand an excessive amount of flexibility, and both sets of hands can be used freely and in an optimal position for additional stimulation.

6. The Bird Of Love

The woman is positioned so that she is lying on her back with her legs raised above her head and a slight bend in her knees (she may need a cushion under her bottom to make it more comfortable). After that, the man gets into her by kneading in between her legs and grabbing her ankles while he does so.

Penetration that is both relatively simple and profound

7. The Explorer

An unplanned sexual encounter might go quite well in this posture. Both the guy and the woman stand facing one another, and the man uses his penis to stimulate the woman's genitals before penetrating the woman.

A simple posture to achieve if the woman is at the same height as the man (or is wearing heels), but if she is not, a table or work surface will be of assistance!

8. The PussyFoot

A simple sex position that requires little effort and makes things tighter.

The man is on his back with his legs together, and the woman is on top of him with her legs together. Then, as she moves up and down on his body, he can get inside her.

And try this great tip: keeping your socks on could make it more likely that you'll have an orgasm.

9. The Grasp

He takes a standing position, and she supports him by wrapping her legs around his waist while he holds her bottom and her back. She can do this to get extra support and a more in-depth massage by leaning her back against a wall.

Although it is perfect for having sex at any time or place, it does demand a certain amount of strength and energy from both the man and the woman participating.

10. The Tominagi

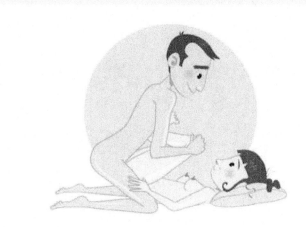

The man is kneeling down, and the woman is lying on her back with her feet propped up on the man's chest. The guy is in control of the penetration, which can go to great depths. This is the ideal position for men with fewer sexual assets.

11. The Seated Ball

This role involves a high level of strength as well as the ability to be flexible.

The woman lowers herself into the man's lap and controls the penetration by rocking back and forth on her heels. Meanwhile, the man enjoys the sensation.

12. The spooning, from-behind sex position

Also Called the Curled Position, While the man spoons the woman from behind, the woman rolls into a ball with her knees drawn up to her chest. This is a terrific posture to be in if you are in the mood to be lazy, and it is also beneficial for pregnant women; the expectant mother only needs to bend her knees slightly so that there is room for her growing belly.

13. The Glowing Juniper

The position that the woman is demonstrating here is ideal for when you want to take it easy; she is lying on her back with her legs spread apart and her knees bent just a little bit. The gentleman occupies a seated position in the middle of her legs, with his legs stretched out on each side of her. While she relaxes and takes it easy, he can then elevate her hips to make it easier for him to penetrate her.

14. The Cross

The woman is positioned so that she is lying on her back with one leg extended and the other leg elevated in the air while bent in half. The male will then straddle the woman's extended leg while maintaining control of the penetration by holding onto the other of her legs.

Simple to do and a wonderful option for when the woman is feeling exhausted.

15. The Perch

The guy will either be seated on a stool or chair, and the woman will sit on the man's lap. By turning her back to him and moving back and forth on her heels, she can control the degree to which he penetrates her. After that, he is free to play with her clitoris and breasts anyway he pleases.

A comfortable position for males who are feeling fatigued as well as pregnant women.

16. The Plough

The woman is currently sitting on the edge of the bed with her legs hanging off of it. After that, he places himself in the space between her legs and lifts her hips and thighs so that he can penetrate her while she props herself up on her elbows.

This position calls for an exceptionally high level of both strength and mobility.

17. The Toad

While the woman lies on her back with her legs spread apart, the man slowly penetrates her while he is positioned between her legs. She can achieve a deeper level of closeness with him by wrapping her legs over him and using her feet to apply light pressure on his buttocks, which will prevent the pressure from causing him to grind his teeth.

It's easy to do, and it's the perfect sex position for taking things at a more leisurely pace.

18. The Hero

The woman is positioned so that she is lying on her back with her knees drawn up to her chest and her feet pointing up toward the ceiling. While he is inside her, the man knelts down and places his belongings under her buttocks.

This is a simple posture, but because the woman needs to hold her legs in the air for longer, she is likely to tire out before the guy.

19. The Peg

While the man is lying on his side, the woman curls up into a ball and places her head at his feet while wrapping her legs around his. She does this while the male continues to rest on his side. The next step is for her to wrap her arms around the top of his legs so that he can penetrate her while she is in this position.

A challenging posture to master, but one that is well worth the additional effort.

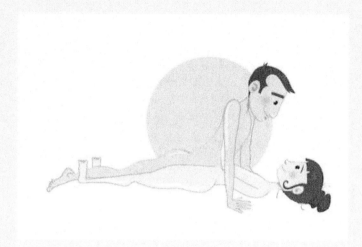

21. The Fan

The woman is hunched down, her back turned to her companion as she crosses her arms and props her elbows on the back of a chair for support. The male then enters her from behind (which is perfect for anal intercourse), and by holding the tops of her thighs, he is able to regulate the depth and pressure of the penetration.

22. The Snail

The lady gets on her back and brings her knees to her chest while she is doing this exercise. The man kneels down and penetrates her. Then, she will be able to prop her feet up on his shoulders, and he will be able to support himself by placing his hands on either side of her shoulders.

Because the penetration is so profound while he is in his sex position, you need to be careful not to move too quickly or you risk causing the woman discomfort.

23. The Slip

While the male is on his knees and leans back, supporting himself with his hands behind him, the woman is lying on her back in a completely horizontal position. After that, she brings her hips closer to him in order to make it easier for him to penetrate her, and she positions her legs on each side of his hips.

This is a rather simple position, yet it offers a lot of erotomania and a good deal of penetration.

24. The Hound

Comparable to the doggy style, with the exception that the woman lowers herself onto her forearms rather than getting down on all fours while the male penetrates her from behind. In addition to this, he can bend forward, and because his hands will be free, he will be able to caress her body at the same time.

25. The Crouching Tiger

The man is lying on the bed with his knees hanging off the side, and the lady is squatting over him with her back turned to him. She has complete command over both the depth and the speed of the penetration.

This sexual position is simple for the guy to assume, but the woman needs to have fairly strong thighs and must be careful not to lose her balance and fall off the bed. The man can easily assume this position. Good luck!

26. The Hinge

Once you get used to the rhythm, this posture offers excellent depth control but necessitates that you have decent balance.

The male knelts down behind the woman and, while he is doing so, leaned backwards and supported himself with one arm. The woman gets down on her knees in front of him and props herself up on her elbows, which enables her to push back against him. After that, he can use the hand he doesn't need to touch her.

27. The Ship

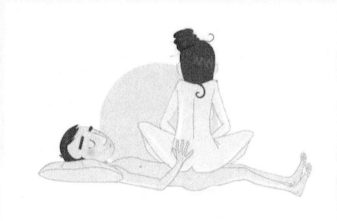

While the male is lying on his back in a flat position, the lady merely sits on top of him with both legs pointing in one direction. The woman maintains full command of the situation. Perfect for times when the man is feeling fatigued or sluggish.

Having a stimulator that you can hold in your hand can also provide another dimension,

28. From Behind

The man approaches the woman from behind and then enters her. The thrusts are under his command at this point. It is possible that leaning against a wall will make it simpler for her to maintain her balance.

This sexual position is simple for some people, but it does not function very well if the two of you are not of comparable heights.

29. Balancing Act

While the male is lying on his back with his legs spread wide, the lady is seated in the space between his thighs. Next, the man must hold the woman while she rolls her body into a tight ball while she does this exercise. She is free to touch herself or touch his perineum with her hands at any time.

Both parties are going to need to bring their A game to the table if they want to maintain this position.

30. Splitting Bamboo

The woman is lying on her back with one leg extended in front of her and the other one resting on the shoulder of her companion. The man has positioned himself so that he is straddling her thigh and is clinging to her raised leg for support.

A comfortable position that makes it possible for the lady to fondle either herself or her partner with both of her hands.

31. The Frog

The man has his feet propped up on the floor while sitting on the edge of the bed, and the woman is crouching on his lap in the position of a frog. She can then move up and down to regulate the penetration while pressing on his thighs for support. This allows her to maintain her position.

The guy has the advantage in this position, but the lady must maintain her strength and equilibrium to win.

32. The Column

The couple's arms are entwined as the woman faces the man while standing in front of him with her back to him. After that, the man is able to elude the woman by approaching her from behind. It might be more convenient for the woman to lean on a table.

34. The Basket

The man maintains his equilibrium by sitting with one leg extended in front of him while the other leg is bowed at the knee. The woman is currently occupying his lap. Although she has the ability to control the majority of the movement, he also has some influence over it thanks to the fact that his hands are on her hips. While they are having sexual relations, he is also in the perfect position to kiss and suck her nipples.

35. The Galley

The man is sitting with his legs spread out in front of him while he rests his weight on one arm (the other is free to be fondled). The woman is seated on top of him at this point and is hunched forward. She is able to prop herself up with her arms at this point, all while maintaining complete control over the movement and the penetration.

A comfortable position that is suitable for both a weary man and an active lady.

36. The Clip

While the man lies on his back and crosses his legs, the lady sits astride him and leans back, supporting herself on her arms. The male shuts his legs. She will then be able to exert her dominance over him as he relaxes and takes it easy.

37. The Whisper

The male is lying on his side as the woman crosses her ankles and wraps her legs over his waist. He is receiving massage therapy. After that, he is free to push in and push out.

38. The Challenge

A stable chair or stool and a lot of balancing ability are both necessities for this position. While doing so, the male approaches the woman from behind while she is squatting on the stool. In order to prevent her from falling over, he will need to maintain a strong grip on her waist.

39. The Kneel

Both the woman and the male will be kneeling as they engage in this sexual position. The sexual act begins when the lady places her legs on each side of the man's, allowing him to penetrate her. They are able to embrace one another with their arms around one another.

A position that isn't too difficult but still requires a lot of passion.

Men can purchase penis rings that help them maintain an erection for a longer period of time.

40. The Kneeling Wheelbarrow

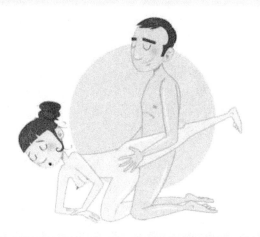

The Kneeling Wheelbarrow is a variation on the Standing Wheelbarrow that is a little bit simpler to operate. The woman is crouching down on one knee while keeping her other leg extended. After that, she shifts her weight such that her elbow is facing the opposite direction as the leg that she is kneeling on, and her companion kneels behind her. While the guy is entering the lady, he might assist her in maintaining her balance by holding her hips.

Be aware that this is a highly taxing position for the woman, so make sure that you don't push yourself too far if you decide to try it.

41. The Spider

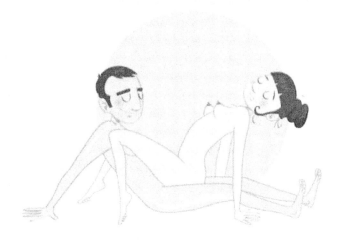

The gentleman is seated with his legs spread apart and his back supported by his hands. The woman is seated astride the man with her back to him. In addition to this, she supports her weight on her hands and can use them to help her rock from side to side.

42. The Fold

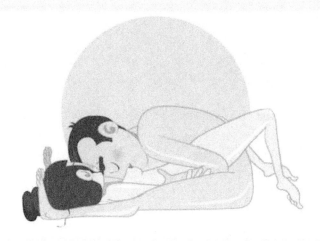

The woman is positioned such that her hips are elevated by placing a cushion beneath her bottom while she is lying on her back. The woman sits with her legs dangling behind her boyfriend's back while the man sits behind her with his legs stretched out on each side of her.

If neither of you have much energy, this is the perfect sex position for you.

43. The Sphinx

The woman is positioned so that she is lying on her front with her weight supported by her elbows. She flexes her second leg to the side while extending the other leg outward. As he leans on his hands for support, the man lays on top of the obstacle, allowing him to approach it from behind.

This is a position that is taxing on the male, but it is well worth it for the woman since the pressure of his body on her pelvis enables her to climax.

44. The Deckchair

The gentleman is seated with his legs spread apart and his back supported by his hands. The woman reclines on her back with her back turned to him. She places a pillow under her bottom so that she may put her feet comfortably on his shoulders.

This is an excellent sex position for achieving a deeper level of penetration.

45. The Waterfall

While the male occupies a seat on a chair or stool, the woman occupies the man's lap. After he has begun to penetrate her, she immediately leans back, and if required, she can rest her head on a cushion that is placed on the floor. Meanwhile, he maintains complete control over every aspect of the action.

This endeavor is not for the faint of heart! This sexual position calls for a significant amount of strength as well as flexibility.

46. The Double Decker

When moving from one sexual position to another, the double decker is an excellent choice because it allows for a smooth transition.

While the male is lying on his back, the lady places herself on top of him and faces away from him. She braces herself on her elbows, which are placed on either side of the man's waist, and she places her feet on the man's knees in order to maintain her balance.

47. The Dolphin

The male positions himself in the space between the woman's legs as the woman is lying on her back. Following that, he lifts her up by the waist so that all of her weight is distributed evenly across her head and shoulders.

This is a sex position that is reasonably easy to get into, but it can be difficult to hold for an extended period of time because the woman may become uncomfortable.

48. The Reverse Cowgirl

The guy performs the reverse cowgirl by lying on his back, while the lady sits astride him with her back to him. This position is known as the "reverse cowgirl." The woman maintains complete command over each and every movement.

A straightforward sexual position that may be performed by nearly anyone. I say, why not give it a shot?

50. The Amazon

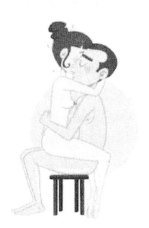

The male will sit on a chair, and it is important that the chair not be too high because the woman's feet need to be able to touch the ground. The woman sits on his lap with her back to him and bounces up and down on his lap using her feet.

Take pleasure in the fact that this sex position gives your thighs a terrific workout.

51. The Close-Up

Both the man and the woman are laying on their sides with their knees drawn up to their chests in the same position. The woman turns her back on the man and lowers her hips into his crotch while maintaining eye contact with him.

A highly relaxed and comfortable sexual position that can also be very close and personal.

52. The Star

The woman is laying on her back with one leg extended and the other leg raised in a bent position. The man maneuvers himself in between her legs and lifts her hips by shoving one of his legs underneath her while simultaneously sliding in between her legs. The man, in an effort to maintain his equilibrium, leans back on his hands.

53. The Indian Handstand

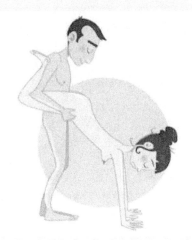

This is a very difficult posture, and the lady must possess a considerable deal of strength as well as balance in order to hold it.

The male maintains his standing position while the woman performs a headstand. The man approaches the woman from the back and assists her in maintaining her balance by grabbing hold of her hips.

54. The Rocking Horse

The individual is seated with his legs crossed and leans back, supporting his weight with his arms while he does so. The woman is seated atop him with her knees bent on both sides of his waist. After then, the woman can rock back and forth, mimicking the action of a rocking horse.

56. Ascent to Desire

The male is standing tall with a very tiny bend in his knees, and the woman is facing him as she does so. After that, he raises her off the ground, and while he is penetrating her, she wraps her arms and legs around his neck while she is being lifted off the ground.

It could be simpler to begin with the man seated, and after he is in the appropriate posture, you can have him stand.

57. The Standing Wheelbarrow

Another difficult position that necessitates a high level of balance and a great deal of talent.

The woman will begin by getting down on all fours; if she finds it more comfortable, she can prop a pillow under her elbows. After bending down behind the woman, the male approaches her and kisses her. After he has sexually penetrated the woman, he will be able to gradually raise her off the ground by grabbing hold of her ankles.

58. Doggy Style

A traditional pose that can be performed by almost anyone.

The couple is in the process of making love when the woman gets down on all fours and supports her weight with her hands while her partner comes up behind her. Even if the woman has the ability to push back against the man, he is still in charge of the majority of the movement.

59. The Nirvana

The woman assumes this kamasutra sex position by lying on her back with her legs closed and her arms extended to the sides of the bed, gripping onto the bedposts (if possible).

The man lays on top of her and positions his legs so that they are next to hers on both sides. While her legs are still crossed, he begins to slowly into her.

60. The Padlock

The lady assumes this sutra sex position by sitting on the edge of a high piece of furniture, such as a table or a washing machine, in order to engage in sexual activity. She adopts a relaxed posture and props herself up with her arms. The man is positioned so that he is facing her. As he enters her, she is able to wrap her legs around his waist and hold them there.

61. The Rock 'n' Roller

The woman rests on her back with a cushion behind her head while the two people are making passionate love to one another. She then brings her legs up into the air and rocks backwards, giving the impression that she is going to perform a backwards roll. While entering her, the male kneels behind her and props her hips up on his thighs. This allows him to more easily reach her private areas.

62. The Backward Slide

The man is propping himself up by sitting on the edge of the bed with a cushion behind his back. His legs are dangling down in front of him. The woman climbs onto his back and lowers herself until her thighs are parallel to his shoulders. She then bends her knees. She then very slowly and gently leans back, and in order to maintain her balance, she places her hands on the ground on either side of his feet.

63. The Crossed Keys

The woman assumes one of the more straightforward kamasutra sexual postures by lying on her back with her legs raised in the air. It is imperative that she sleeps with her bottom resting on the edge of the bed while her legs are crossed. The man stands facing her while he penetrates her and grabs hold of her legs with both hands.

An easy sex position.

64. The Ape

Give this position a shot if you're looking for something a little bit out of the ordinary.

The man is prone on the ground and brings his knees to his chest. While the woman turns her back to her partner, the man sits with his feet on her back and penetrates her while she is seated on top of him. The woman relies on her feet to maintain her balance and exert control over the movement.

Excellent for penetrating to a deep level.

65. The Reclining Lotus

The woman must have a considerable level of flexibility in order to maintain this posture, which requires her to lay on her back with her legs crossed.

While he is inside her, the man lays on top of her and uses his arms to maintain his balance.

66. Wide Opened

The lady is currently resting on her back with a pillow placed directly beneath her head. The man enters her by kneading in the space between her legs, then sliding his thighs under her back to lift her hips while he does so.

Are you up for some excitement in the water? Even while taking a shower or bath, you and your spouse can stimulate one another with the help of Dulux's Vibrating Bullet.

67. The Peg

The man is laying on his back with his legs spread out and extended out in front of him. The woman is currently positioned so that she is laying on top of him with her legs crossed and extended.

Because the woman's legs are closed, this is an excellent sex position for well-endowed partners, as the guy will not be able to penetrate the lady too deeply. Additionally beneficial to intimacy due to the fact that you are face to face.

68. Indrani

A pillow is tucked in behind the woman's head while she rests on her back. She brings her knees to her chest and allows the man to glide between her legs while he does so. The lady is able to bring the male closer to her and maintain her level of control over the sexual encounter.

69. Suspended Congress

While he is pulling the woman off the ground and holding her by placing his hands under her bottom, the man leans on a wall for support. The woman's thighs are able to secure a hold on the man's waist.

Demands effort and fortitude from both sides, but the rewards more than justify the trouble.

70. The Suspended Scissors

Caution: maintaining your balance and strength while holding this position is absolutely essential.

The woman is positioned so that she is lying on the very edge of the bed, with only her feet resting on the surface of the mattress for support. After that, she uses her left arm to maintain her balance while standing on the floor. The man balances himself on her left thigh while simultaneously lifting her right thigh with his hands.

A little bit difficult, but not too challenging after you get into position.

71. The Propeller

This one is not going to be helpful for everyone in any way. In point of fact, it will only work if the male in question possesses extraordinarily large breasts.

The woman is laying on her back with her legs crossed and her arms at her sides. The man is laying on top of her as she is facing the opposite direction from where he is. Once he is completely inside of her, he will be able to softly move his hips in a circular fashion.

72. The Prone Tiger

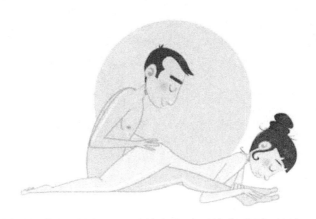

The gentleman is currently seated on the bed, and he has his legs spread apart in front of him. The woman positions herself so that she is facing forward, separates her legs, and then backs into the guy so that she may drop herself onto his penis. It is proper for the woman to have her legs spread apart behind the male.

73. The Crisscross

The male is lying next to the woman, who is laying on her side with her back turned away from him. Her legs are slightly apart. The male will similarly lay on his side, but will do so perpendicular to the lady. He will then glide in between her legs in order to enter her.

74. The Erotic V

The male is positioned such that he is facing the woman while she is seated at the table's edge. It is necessary for the lady to bring her legs all the way up and place the backs of her knees on the shoulders of the male. She can also provide support by wrapping her arms around his neck, and he can assist in motion control by grabbing her bottom with his hands.

75. The Catherine Wheel

Both the man and the woman take seats facing one another. During the process of him entering her, she wraps her legs around his waist and holds them there. After that, he puts one of his legs around her waist and squeezes. A lady can keep her balance by resting her weight on her arms, while a guy can do the same by leaning on his elbows.

Mastering this sex position might be somewhat challenging.

76. The Triumph Arch

This position requires a woman who is very flexible because the lady needs to be in a position in which she is lying on her back with her legs bent underneath her. The man then positions himself in such a way that he is able to slide in between her legs, with his legs stretched out to the sides of her head. Afterwards, he continues to maneuver himself so that he can successfully complete the task.

77. The X-Rated

As part of the medical treatment he is receiving, the patient is positioned on his stomach with a pillow supporting his head. The man is currently being covered by a woman who is lying on top of him with her back turned away from him, her legs placed on either side of his waist, and her arms wrapped around his legs. While she enjoys a view that is perfect for gliding up and down, he is subjected to a perspective that is not conducive to productive work.

78. The Shoulder Stand

The man lends his assistance to the woman as she lies on her back and simultaneously lifts both of her legs as well as her upper body into the air. The man kneels behind her as she is resting her legs on his shoulders, and while he is doing so, he approaches her while he is kneeling there.

If you want to get the most out of this particular sexual position, you should go easy on each other.

79. The Rowing Boat

The man is supposed to start the position by lying back, and the woman is supposed to sit astride him. Starting off in this manner is the most productive way to approach the position. After he has started to penetrate her, the male may start to slowly sit up so that they are facing each other with their legs intertwined. This position is known as the "face-to-face position." They can increase their level of comfort by sitting in this position with their arms tucked underneath the legs of the person sitting next to them.

80. The Zen Pause

When you need to take things at a more leisurely pace during a lengthy sex session, this is the position to be in.

Both the man and the woman laid down on their sides with their backs to one another. As the woman wraps her legs around the man, the man walks into the woman.

81. The Landslide

Because of the angles, a man who is already well endowed is the best candidate for this position.

The woman is positioned so that she is lying on her stomach, with her legs extended, and her torso is propped up by resting on her elbows. The gentleman is seated in such a way that he is facing the back of her head while facing her legs. His legs are separated on either side of her waist. While he is entering her, he props himself up with his hands behind him and tilts his body at a slight angle. He does this so that he can get closer to her.

82. The Supernova

This sex position is a slight variation of the traditional woman-on-top, but in this case, the man lays with the top half of his body handing off the edge of the bed, and the woman sits astride him and leans back onto her arms for support. Alternatively, the man may lay with the top half of his body handing off the edge of the bed..

Be cautious so that you do not fall off the side of the bed.

83. The Squat Balance

The woman is positioned so that she is standing on the bed, and the man is standing behind her. He places his hands on her bottom, and she eases herself down onto him while he holds them there. After that, he is able to penetrate her while she is using his arms to stabilize herself.

84. The Shoulder Holder

The woman is positioned so that she is lying on her back with a pillow under her head and her legs raised in the air in a vertical position. While he is penetrating her on his knees, the man grips her legs and rests them on one of his shoulders while he continues to perform the act. He is able to support himself with his other hand.

Ideal for penetrating to a great depth.

85. The Seduction

You should only attempt this position if you have a lot of
flexibility; the woman is lying on her back with her legs bent
underneath her body. After that, the man will sexually
penetrate the woman by laying on top of her.

86. The Lustful Leg

Another one of those positions that calls for a great deal of adaptability.

Both the man and the woman are standing with their backs to one another. The first thing that the woman does is position her leg on the bed so that the man can get into her. Once they are inside, he can gradually assist her in climbing onto his shoulder by supporting her leg.

Take care not to lose your footing and fall over as you navigate this obstacle!

87. The Glowing Triangle

The standard missionary position has been given a new name—the glowing triangle position—that is both straightforward and remarkably efficient.

The man will move on top of the woman as she is laying on her back in this position. But instead of lying on top of her, he gets down on all fours, and she has to lift her pelvis in order for him to be able to have sexual relations with her. After that, he is to remain motionless while she completes all of the work..

88. The Y Curve

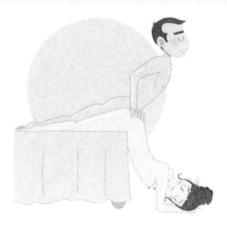

A fairly precarious position that calls for the man's full strength and composure to be effective in.

The woman flips over onto her stomach on the bed and allows the upper half of her body to hang off the side of the mattress. It's possible that she needs something to rest her head on, like a pillow. The man positions himself so that he is able to pierce her while he is laying between her legs, and then he pushes his body up so that he is not laying on her back.

89. The Magic Mountain

To begin, you will need to construct your "mountain" by piling a stack of firm pillows on top of one another. The woman then gets down on her knees and bends over the pillows until her chest is resting completely on the cushions. The man gets on his knees behind her and then inserts his legs on either side of her to deeply penetrate her.

90. The Laptop

The gentleman is seated in a chair with a pillow tucked in between his knees in order to raise them. The woman climbs up onto his lap and raises her legs to the point where they are encircling his neck. After that, the man can support the woman's back with his hands while the woman rocks back and forth on his penis.

91. The Stair Master

If you hadn't already guessed it from the position's name, you'll need some stairs to achieve this particular sexual position.

While the woman kneels on one step, her partner kneels a couple steps lower and approaches her from behind. She can brace herself against the step in front of her or the banister if she feels unsteady, but the man can easily penetrate her by simply holding on to her hips as he does so.

92. The Mermaid

The woman is lying down on a table with her bottom resting on the very edge of the surface. The next step is for her to stand with both of her legs in the air while the man stands behind her and penetrates her. If she finds it more comfortable, she can place a pillow beneath her bottom. He can provide himself with additional stability by holding onto her feet in this position.

93. The Sidekick

The man is facing the woman who is laying on her side with her back to him. He gets on his knees behind her, turns his back to her, and enters her by straddling her leg. He is facing her head. After that, she opens up more space for him to maneuver by extending her top leg outward.

94. The Thigh Master

The man is positioned so that he is lying on his back with his legs bent and slightly separated from one another. The woman is positioned so that she is facing away from the man while she is straddling one of his thighs. Then, while keeping her body at a slight angle, she grabs onto his knees and slowly lowers herself onto him. Eventually, she is on top of him.

95. The Butterfly

The butterfly position is very similar to the mermaid position in that it involves the woman having sex while laying on a relatively low table with her bottom right on the edge of the table. The man stands and uses his hands to assist the woman in lifting her hips. While she lies with her legs propped up on his shoulders, he makes love to her.

96. The Sideways Samba

The woman is positioned so that she is lying on her side with her legs positioned in front of her at an angle of ninety degrees. It is necessary for her to rotate her pelvis inwards as the man lays behind her and raises his torso using an arm on either side of his waist as support while he penetrates her. He will then proceed to do so.

97. The Side Saddle

A simple sexual position that doesn't require a lot of work and is perfect for when you want to try something new but don't want to exert too much effort.

The gentleman is currently resting on his back with a pillow placed directly behind his head and his legs spread apart. The woman is seated so that she is facing him and her legs are propped up on one side of his waist while her hands are propped up on the other side, supporting her weight. While he is penetrating her, she can slowly open and close her legs and make swiveling motions to drive him crazy. This will make him want to do whatever she wants.

98. The Proposal

Both the man and the woman are crouching down with their backs against each other (it helps if you are similar heights). He prepares to propose by placing one foot on the ground, and she responds by placing the other foot on the ground in preparation for the beginning of the act of penetration.

It's possible that you'll need to shift around a bit before you can find a comfortable position.

A sex position that is not overly difficult and is beneficial if you are looking to try something different.

99. The G-Force

The woman assumes a sex position in which she lies on her back and brings both of her knees all the way up to her chest. The man kneels behind her and lifts her torso off the ground, bringing it level with his thighs so that her back is perpendicular to his. She is able to keep her balance by holding onto his legs, while he is able to penetrate her by holding onto her feet and holding onto her legs.

100. The Right Angle

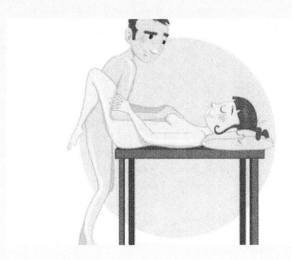

In the Right Angle sex position, the lady is positioned such that she is lying on her back, with her bottom resting on the edge of the bed or table.

While entering her, her lover fondles either her breasts or clitoris before initiating sexual contact.

The Right Angle position is equally effective when there is no thrusting involved. If the woman seizes hold of the man by crossing her ankles behind his back and the guy forces himself against her, the pressure will build, and both participants will experience an incredible rush of pleasure as a result.

If she is able to contract the muscles on the floor of her pelvis, this may be a highly exciting posture.

Best Kamasutra Positions to Try Out

Some of the postures described in the Kama Sutra are somewhat unconventional and call for a certain level of physical prowess as well as flexibility. Nevertheless, there are a great many of them that are simple enough that almost anybody may attempt them. Experiment with these easy but pleasant sex positions from the Kama Sutra:

– The Rider –

Afternoon Delight –

The Visitor (use a table or chair to make it easier) –

The Slide –

The Tominagi –

The Curled Angel –

The Toad –

The Reverse Cowgirl –

The Close Up –

The Nirvana –

The Crossed Keys –

The Side Saddle (use a table or chair to make it easier) –

The Toad –

The Reverse Cowgirl –

The Close-

Which sexual positions in the Kamasutra are the most challenging?

The Kama Sutra describes a variety of more sophisticated sexual positions that call for a great degree of balance, strength, and flexibility from the couple performing them. They may be difficult to master, but that doesn't mean you can't have fun trying - just be careful not to injure yourself by stretching your body beyond what it's capable of doing!

The following are some of the most challenging sexual positions described in the Kama Sutra:

– The Bridge

– The Plough

– Balancing Act

– The Challenge

– The Waterfall

The Kama Sutra

– The Indian Handstand

– The Standing Wheelbarrow

– Suspended Congress

– The Suspended Scissors

– The Lustful Leg

Printed in Great Britain
by Amazon

57077759R00059